The
Inspired Teacher's
Journal

The
Inspired
Teacher's Journal

A Weekly Guide to Becoming Your Best Self

by

Michele Vosberg, Ph.D.

& Paula Schmidt, Ed.D.

First Printing: March 2021

ISBN: 978-1-7362273-1-2

Disclaimer:

This book is designed to provide practical and applicable content regarding the subject covered. Neither the authors nor publisher is engaged in rendering legal, financial, medical or other professional advice. If expert assistance is required, the services of a professional should be sought.

Inspired Together Learning
P.O. Box 8291
3903 Milwaukee St.
Madison, WI 53708

For the teachers who have taught us,
we are forever grateful.

For the teachers we have taught with,
you inspire us every day.

For the teachers we have taught,
and for the those we will teach,
we are honored to be part of your journey.

Introduction

Welcome to your best teacher life!

If you have picked up this book, you are likely a teacher who *cares*. You care deeply about your students and want to be good at what you do. You want to be a teacher who makes a difference. You work hard and give much of yourself. You are likely a leader and give your time and energy for the greater good of your school, district or the wider community.

Teaching can be incredibly rewarding, but it can also be incredibly demanding.

Let's face it, sometimes being an exceptional teacher comes at the cost of your personal life. **You want to be good at your job, but you also want a fulfilling life outside of school.** You have family and friends and relish time with them. You want time to enjoy the simple things, like time with your pet or time to read a good book. You also want and need time for your own mental and physical health.

Our profession asks much of us, and we ask much of ourselves. Finding balance is an ongoing struggle. It is somewhat like walking a tightrope while carrying a long balancing stick. In addition to teaching, you may also function as a nurse, social worker, counselor, mentor, or advisor. You answer to the many demands of your students, their parents, your administrators, and your community.

Given all that is asked of teachers, how do we stay present and purposeful? How can we be proactive and not reactive? How do we live with gratitude and stay optimistic in a world where many things scream for our attention?

If there was an easy answer to these questions, there would be no teacher burnout. We would no longer lose so many talented, caring, teachers because they are exhausted and drained of everything that they can possibly give.

As long-time educators, we know that the path towards living a satisfying life comes through living with intention. Rather than letting life come at you and reacting to the many demands placed on you, you learn to make choices that serve you. Living the life you deserve is about deciding what you want and need and how you can bring your best self to your work without sacrificing your personal life.

What does it take for teachers to live with intention?

First of all, we have to have a vision of what we want in our lives. How can you ever be satisfied with your life if you don't know how you want to live?

To live with intention, we also need to use our unique gifts, talents, and skills. Rather than imitate others, we are at our best when we know who we are, what we bring to the world, and how we can work within our own unique genius.

No one's life is without obstacles and challenges. Rather than letting challenges derail us, we need to learn to recognize them, eliminate them when we can, and when we can't eliminate them, meet them head on.

We also need to develop habits and actions that will support us in being our best. How we manage our time, the habits that we engage in automatically, and the choices we make in what we do and how we do it can help us or hinder us.

Lastly, we all need our own star system, a support system of others who will listen and enrich us in life-giving ways.

This book is designed to guide you in living your life, both your teaching life AND your personal life, with intention. We'll help you describe your vision and identify your unique gifts and talents. We'll ask you to look for obstacles and challenges and make a plan for dealing with them. We will assist you in setting up daily and weekly habits and actions that will support you in the lifestyle you want. And we will encourage you to recognize when you need support and figure out who in your teaching or personal life would be best to help you.

In the next chapters, we will explain the process, and the reasons behind the questions you will answer and the work you will do. This book was not designed to be read passively. It was designed to be interactive. We know you have been taught not to write in books, but this book is made for your writing. Grab your favorite pen or your colorful Sharpies and get ready to mess up this book.

We want you to mark up the pages. Go ahead and underline the parts that speak to you. Go crazy with your highlighter. Most importantly, write your answers to the questions we've asked. This is where the thinking happens, and that thinking that has the power to change your life.

We've also included words of wisdom and quotes from real teachers throughout this book. They are there to inspire you and to make you think. We've always believed in the power that exists when engaged and inspired teachers work together.

The second half of this book is made up of pages for you to use each week in order to plan your week with intention.

We recognize that doing the work of this journal is potentially adding one more thing to a plate that is already full. However, we are also confident that the time you spend doing this work will provide a life-changing return on your investment. Rather than drifting through your days in a state of overwhelm, you will be proactive in designing your days.

It is our sincere hope and vision that we all live with intention and design a life that is of our own choosing. We applaud you for caring enough about yourself, and your quest for your best life, to take on this challenge.

We look forward to this journey with you!

Our best,

Paula and Michele

Chapter 1

The Promise and the Reality

How would you describe your typical day? If you are like many teachers, it probably sounds something like this:

You get up and rush around, trying to get ready for school. You have a busy day with multiple classes, each requiring significant prep time. After a full day of teaching, you have a staff meeting. After school, you optimistically fill a bag with work to take home, even though deep down you know that you will drag it back to school undone. In the evening, you hope to get in a workout, relax, spend a little time with your family or friends, and then get a good night's sleep. You end up watching TV, scrolling on your phone, grading a handful of papers, and then collapsing, exhausted, into bed.

Some days are much better. On a good morning, you have already prepared a healthy lunch and set out clean, comfortable, professional clothes. You've done your morning workout and filled your travel mug with coffee to drink on your commute to school. You get to school in time to finish a few last-minute details, say hello to a colleague, and welcome your class with enthusiasm.

In reality, those blissful mornings are few and far between. On your worst mornings, you hit the snooze button one too many times, and now you're running late. You take the dog out…but she won't go. You didn't get your meal prepping done, so you grab an apple and an energy bar and throw them in your bag. You realize, too late, that you don't have anything comfortable and clean to wear and your clothes are just a hot mess. To make matters worse, on the drive to school your coffee spills, leaving a noticeable stain on your shirt. You grab a sweater from the back seat and put it on. It is not perfect, but it is better than walking around with a stained shirt.

On a good day, your classes run smoothly. Your lessons plans are well written and well received. You and your students are having fun. During your prep time you get the next day's lessons planned and the papers graded. Later in the day, a parent stops by and thanks you for helping their child. You feel appreciated. You know the work you are doing is valuable and you feel fulfilled. This is the promise and the dream, this is what you signed on for.

In reality, your days don't always look like the dream. Your lessons sometimes don't work as planned. There are days when students are disengaged at best and uncooperative at worst. A struggle with a defiant, out of control student drains you. An emergency on the playground followed by an unexpected parent phone call consumes your entire prep time. At the end of the day, the staff meeting drags on and on.

After school, you are exhausted. You meant to stay at work and get some things done, followed by a work-out. What you really want is a bag of chips and time to go to the bathroom. Once again you throw all the unfinished work in your bag and head for home.

That bag full of unfinished work is a symbol for the struggles of a teacher. It represents both optimism and pain.

There is always more to do than the time we have to do it. A teacher's to-do list is never finished. There is always another lesson plan, another student issue, another meeting and another set of papers to grade. Teaching is complicated by the fact that we are also dealing with real students with real needs and priorities that are ever shifting.

Rest assured that you aren't the only one who has hauled home a bag full of work only to haul it back the next day untouched. Carrying around the weight of all of that untouched work, and all of those unfinished plans and projects, leaves us feeling overwhelmed and stressed. And if that isn't enough, guilt rears its ugly head. If you were going to design your best life, would you include overwhelm, stress and guilt? Of course not, but that is often what happens.

Finding a balance between all the work of our school lives and the plans we have for our personal lives is likely the number one cause of disillusionment for teachers.

The reality of teaching doesn't always align with our expectations. Here is a typical scenario. One of your students experiences many deep challenges. You recognize that there are many things about the student's home and family life that you cannot control. However, you know that this student needs you desperately and that you can make a difference in his life.

So, you pour love and attention into the student, and the student thrives. It is every teacher's dream to make a difference in the lives of their students, and your dream has been fulfilled. This is an example of how teachers answer their calling with their highest and best work.

And yet, this success comes at a cost. The teacher's inner questions are always there, causing overwhelm, stress and guilt. What are the things I didn't have time to do as I was giving extra help to this student? How many hours of my personal time did I spend, worrying, counseling, and creating extra plans for this student? What plans and goals of my own did I give up? Who else in my life may have gotten shortchanged?

These are the emotional struggles that challenge us. How we learn to deal with them will determine our ongoing satisfaction with teaching.

As veteran teachers with many years of teaching experience between us, we know that there is a way to pour your heart and soul into your job without completely emptying your own bucket.

Imagine what it would be like to spend most of your days feeling contentment. You have created a life and a job that you love. You live with intention and your life feels balanced. You are using your unique gifts and talents in ways that make you feel happy and fulfilled. You've experienced challenges and met them head on. You have let go of unrealistic expectations and ineffective habits. And best of all, you are surrounded with a star system of caring, supportive people who will encourage you, challenge you to rise higher, and lift you up when you need it.

If that sounds like a life you want to sign up for, read on. In the next chapter, we're going to give you the tools to get there.

What lies before us and what lies behind us are small matters compared to what lies within us.
And when we bring what is within out into the world, miracles happen.

Henry David Thoreau

Chapter 2

Designing Your Best Life

We all want to live our best, truest and most fulfilled life.

There are two routes we can take in our lives. One is to be like a leaf in a stream, drifting along, never resisting the current, and ending up wherever the water takes us. This is the path of least resistance.
It's fairly easy to identify people who are drifting. They don't set a lot of goals for their life. They are going through the motions. They take a job, maybe even one they don't like, because it is there. They don't move on because it seems easier not to.

Teachers who are drifting often spend their days reactively dealing with the challenges that appear, but not making the changes that would eliminate some of those challenges in the first place. They often feel unhappy in their work life, personal life, or both. They may feel resentful of others, without recognizing that their continued drifting is of their own choosing. They choose not to or can't see a better way.

Unfortunately, some teachers have found themselves drifting. Some of these teachers went into the field of education not because they had a passion, but because they couldn't think of a different career path they really wanted. They got a teaching job and will tell you with a shrug that their job is "fine." They are generally not invested, and they appear to do the minimum, not fully giving of themselves or their talents. Unfortunately, these teachers may not even be aware of their many talents.

As you have likely observed, teachers who are drifting are not a happy bunch. They may find fault in the students, the parents and the administration but don't take action to make things better. For a variety of reasons, they find themselves reacting to life, not taking charge and making positive change.

The life of a teacher who is drifting is rarely filled with passion or love of the job. In fact, it can be sad place to live. Brendon Burchard, a personal development expert whom we greatly respect, calls this "the caged life." People who are trapped in their own experiences often feel stuck and don't see a way out. The result is living in misery.

The other route, and the most preferable and enjoyable route, is to design a life we love. Designers have a vision of who they are and who they want to be. They have goals and take steps to achieve those goals. They are engaged in their lives and invested in the outcomes. They are proactive in looking at their challenges and trying to minimize them. They create actions and habits that will serve them, and in turn will best serve others.

Designers tend to have a growth mindset. Of course, there are challenges, but they see challenges as a learning opportunity. They keep learning and try to continually grow and become better.

Designers don't let their current circumstances limit their picture of the future. Yes, sometimes they will get stuck and don't get to where they want to be because they don't yet have the right mindset, knowledge, skills or habits. However, those things can be learned. Designers surround themselves with a strong support system so they can ask for and receive help.

It all boils down to choosing what kind of life you want to live. When you have a vision of who you want to be and what's important in

your life, you will find the energy and enthusiasm to take the next steps on your journey to the life you want to live.

Ultimately, we need to ask ourselves a series of difficult questions. Am I a drifter or a designer? What do I want to be in the future, a drifter teacher or a designer teacher? What kind of life will I choose and pursue?

Are you still with us? If you've read this far, all signs indicate that you have the desire, the drive, and the willingness to find and live your best life. Congratulations.

It's time. Let's dig in!

Developing Your Vision

Do you have a vision for your life? Do you know what you want out of life? Do you know who you want to be? These are tough questions. This is going to sound ridiculous, but how are you going to get to wherever you want to be if you don't know where you're going? And if you don't know what you want, how will you know if you've gotten it?

If you don't have a vision for your life, you will drift. Earlier, you determined you were a designer, not a drifter, and designers need a clear vision.

Developing your vision means doing some soul searching. It means looking deep within to discover who and what means the most to you personally. Your vision is your higher purpose. It is your "why." When the going gets tough, having a strong vision will keep you focused and motivated.

The more vividly you can see and feel your vision, the more real it will seem and the harder you will fight for it.

Asking yourself questions such as the following will help you uncover your vision. Spend some quality time with these questions. Step away from your busy life for a few minutes because the answers to these questions are important for establishing a foundation before moving forward. Be honest with yourself. Give yourself grace. Dig deep and describe your answers in as much detail as you can.

If I were to describe my dream day, what would I be doing? Who would I be with? Where would I be?

What kinds of feelings do I want to experience on a daily basis?

What do I love about my current life?

What would I like to change about my current life?

Where or when am I trying to fulfill someone else's dreams for me?
Where or when am I being true to myself?

What do I love to do?

What am I passionate about?

Who needs me?

What is worth fighting for?

When I look back on my life, what will I be proud that I have done?

As you describe your vision of yourself, envision your future with clarity. Feel it. Own it. Get excited about it. Believe that it can happen and believe that you can make it happen.

When you are down to your last nerve,

or feel like you are running in place,

remember why you chose this profession.

Remember your "why."

R.J. Willis

7th and 8th grade Social Studies Teacher

What would the best and truest version of myself look like? What would it sound like? Feel like?

My Vision Board

Use this page and the next pages to sketch, draw, or write your vision for what you want to be, to have, to do, or to feel. Include both your teacher life and personal life. Grab colored markers or pencils. Glue stickers, photos or pictures from magazines. Make it visual, make it fun, and make it your own!

My Vision Board

My Vision Board

Chapter 3

Recognize and Use Your Unique Gifts and Talents

We each have gifts and talents that make us special. Do you have the ability to create a great rapport with people? Can you make people laugh? Maybe you are great at thinking of and creating out-of-the-box activities or maybe you have a quiet gentleness about you that calms students when they are agitated.

Usually, when we are good at something, we like to use those skills. Sometimes we are even passionate about them. Using our gifts and talents feels good, and when we excel at something, we usually find it fun. If we are enjoying our teaching, chances are good that the students will enjoy it too. And let's face it, most classrooms thrive with a little bit of fun!

We've all had a teacher who took subject matter that we might not have been initially interested in and made it exciting. One history teacher talked about the members of royal dynasties as if they were characters in a show called The Real Housewives of the 1700's. Another teacher used his love of music to entice his chemistry students to write funny songs about the elements. We can all think of examples of this from our experiences as a student and as a teacher.

Rather than seeing a teacher that you admire and trying to copy their every move, look at that teacher and see how they are expressing their gifts in their teaching. You will realize that the way to emulate an excellent teacher is not to try to copy everything they do, but to recognize how they use their own personality and unique gifts to make their teaching world a success. Then copy them, not by mimicking their gifts, but instead by tapping into and using your own unique and powerful gifts.

Knowing yourself is the beginning of all wisdom.
Aristotle

Many people do not easily recognize their own gifts and talents. There is a faulty belief that, "if it is easy for me, it must be easy for everyone." That could not be further from the truth. What is it that comes easily for you? What is it that brings you joy? What do you do easily that your colleagues struggle to replicate? The answers to these questions will help you get closer to identifying your unique gifts and talents both in and out of the classroom.

Some gifts and talents are connected to knowledge such as having deep understanding of information in your content area. Your personal talents might also be connected to hobbies or activities you enjoy. You may even find that you have the gift of combining your knowledge and hobbies to share your passion in a way that helps others understand.

Some of your gifts are related to your personality. You might be calm, energetic, curious, joyful, or determined. Maybe you are gifted at connecting people. Others may look to you as a beacon of hope and optimism. Perhaps kindness is your superpower.

If you are struggling to identify your gift and talents, try one of these ideas:

- Text ten friends. Ask them to identify your strengths, gifts, and talents.

- Dig out any personality inventories you have taken, such as StrengthsFinder, The Enneagram, True Colors, or The Myers-Briggs Inventory. What can you learn about yourself?

- Think about those old report card comments. If you read comments about talking too much, you might be naturally social and a great connecter. If you heard that you were bossy, you might really have been demonstrating leadership skills.

- Remember what you loved when you were eight years old, before the world started telling you what was possible. What made you happy? Why? Which skills were you using?

Whatever means you use to determine your strengths and talents, figure out what your special sauce is and use it in your classroom!

Maybe you can share your love of yoga by helping students find peace, harmony, and relaxation through the practice. If you have a green thumb, bring in plants to make your room beautiful and healthier. If you love maps, bring maps into as many lessons and subject areas as possible. Point out where authors lived or where mathematicians were born. If your sense of humor is your superpower, tell a joke or two as students line up for lunch. If you are a doodler at heart, draw cartoons on the board each morning.

The possibilities are endless.

You must be genuine in order to help students be and become their best unique selves. You can't 'be' or 'teach like' someone else. Bring the real YOU to the classroom: your passions, wonderings, joys, challenges, and especially quirks and faults. Your students will know you, trust you, and find safety and inspiration to be themselves, too.

Deb Fordice
Elementary Music Teacher

What gifts, talents, skills and passions do I bring into the world?

What are some ways that I might bring my unique gifts into my classroom?

Chapter 4

Expect the Challenges

Every life and every career will have obstacles and challenges. There is no getting around it, so we might as well accept it and deal with it as best we can. In fact, by reminding ourselves that challenges are a natural part of life, we give ourselves and our students permission for grace and forgiveness when these obstacles occur.

Life hands us some obstacles, others are of our own making. Some we can see coming and others surprise us when we least expect them. If we are not mindful to the challenges in our personal and professional lives and how we react to them, unforeseen obstacles can derail us and make us quit.

Life's obstacles include things we often can't control such as accidents, illness, death of a someone we love, loss of a job, and most recently, the pandemic. **We may not be able to influence, control or prevent the outcome, but we *can* control how we react to it.**

The potholes in the road of life require time, support, and resiliency. They may slow you down or stop you for a time. You may find yourself on an unexpected or unwelcomed detour. All of this is normal. When we are prepared for obstacles and challenges to come our way, we better equip ourselves to work through them and not be stopped by them.

The gremlins in our heads are likely to stop us in our tracks. We each have our own personal gremlins. Our gremlins may be things we learned in childhood or have generalized from our own experiences. They may be deeply ingrained in our value systems. They may slow us down or sabotage us forever if we let them.

Here are some of the gremlins in our heads:

Fear of failure

Fear of judgement

Guilt

Comparison

Perfectionism

Scarcity issues

Imposter syndrome

Fear of success

Does this make you angry at your personal gremlins? Don't be. Our gremlins are trying to protect us in the best way they know how, which is to shut us down. At a basic level, our gremlins keep us safe by instilling fear.

When something is new and unknown, fear is natural. We've learned to respect fear and pay attention. It keeps us safe and alive. In this way, our gremlins are helpful in giving us reminders. We do need to pay attention. However, we also need to recognize when fear is irrational. We need to acknowledge when fear has moved beyond protecting us to actually hindering us. When one of our fears is not serving us, we need to challenge it.

How do you challenge a gremlin?

What works well for you may not work for others but there are some common "gremlin beating behaviors" that work well for most gremlins. Here are some to consider adopting for yourself:

Change your self-talk. Take time to analyze the discussions going on in your head and ask yourself some difficult but important questions. What am I saying to myself? Is it true? What is the evidence that it is or isn't true? Is it is coming from a past negative experience? If so, what is different this time?

Recognize where the negative voice is coming from. Is the voice from your childhood? Your principal? An angry parent? Is it your emotional brain talking or your rational brain talking?

Consider the danger. What is the gremlin warning you of? Is it a real danger? What can you do to mitigate potential danger?

Talk back. Tell your gremlin the truth. Imagine your gremlin is telling you not to try a new teaching method because it might not work, and chaos will ensue. Talk back. Tell your gremlin, "I know I haven't done this before, but I am good at classroom management. If students get off track, I can bring them back. If it doesn't work, I will reevaluate."

Don't let others belittle your ideas. Not everyone will be supportive of you and that is okay. You don't need everyone to be on board. If your gremlin is afraid that others will judge you, don't share your plans with the judgers. Instead, surround yourself with people who will champion your ideas.

Stop comparing yourself to others. Comparison is the thief of joy. Consider where your comparisons are coming from. Turn off your social media if you find you are judging yourself in comparison. Stop looking at perfect classrooms on Pinterest. Be especially careful of comparing yourself to others who are further along on their path.

Stop living to fulfill others' expectations. Your journey is your own. Being who others expect you to be is not the way to fulfill your own dreams. Have some honest conversations with people in your life. Your needs matter, and you will be a better son, daughter, partner, friend, parent, or worker when your own needs are met.

Stop striving to be perfectly "balanced." What does balanced mean to you? Balance does not mean everything in your life gets equal time. It means that each thing gets the time that it needs at the moment. Someone else's version of balance may look nothing like yours and that is perfectly fine.

Eliminate the drama. Stay out of what is not yours. Focus on *your* concerns, worries, responsibilities. Though it often comes from a place of love, stop trying to fix or control everyone or everything.

Adopt a growth mindset rather than a fixed mindset. A growth mindset recognizes that people always grow and change. Mistakes are just part of the process and you learn from them. Mistakes are to be expected, not feared. You don't have to be perfect!

Your gremlins are bound to pop up. The path of least resistance is to let them shut you down. We've all experienced a time when we let our gremlins change our mood, or even change the way we think about ourselves. It is perfectly normal to have a bad day. Bad things happen. But in the end, you can make the choice to let your gremlins defeat you, or you can make the choice to acknowledge them, deal with them, dismiss them, and then move on with confidence.

I often say to people, "Your choices allow you to be part of the problem or the solution."

Stacy Morley
Special Education Teacher

What obstacles, struggles, or mindset issues do I have that might potentially hold me back? These might be obstacles in my personal life or teaching life or both.

What are some of the ways that I might challenge my personal gremlins?

Chapter 5

Develop Good Habits and Actions

What is life made of if not lots and lots of days? How do you spend your days? That will largely determine how you spend your *life.*

If we want to have control of our lives, it follows that we must control our days.

Habits are daily rituals and practices that we put into place. Many habits are small, but they compound over time and eventually have great impact on our lives. Habits often get a bad reputation. We often think of habits as something we must or should do, rather than something we want to do. However, if chosen purposefully, habits can actually give us more time and more freedom.

Structure creates freedom because instead of spending time figuring out what to do, we have habits that become automatic. This allows us to spend our time and energy on things we want to do!

Who doesn't want more time and energy?

Let's start with the most essential habits of all, those regarding our health and wellbeing.

Health and Wellbeing

Consider your habits around health. Are you getting enough sleep? Do you eat healthy food- at least most of the time? Do you drink enough water? What about fresh air and exercise? Consider your mental health as well. Do you have people you can talk to? What about people to laugh with?

Habits around health issues are often difficult. It's hard to do all the right things all the time.

Take a look at your habits in the area of health and wellbeing. **Pick one habit to try to improve.** Write it down and make it a goal that you will follow for one week. When you are doing it consistently, it has become a habit. Then you can try out and create another habit.

Professionalism

What is professionalism if not a habit? Professionalism is showing up, ready to do what you intend to do. Teachers are often measured in terms of professionalism- what you say, how you show up, how you speak with others, and how you act.

Think about your habits connected to professionalism:

How do you spend your time? Are you on-time? Do you show up prepared for meetings? Do you use your time wisely?

Consider your interactions with colleagues. Do you have a habit of greeting people? Do you interact with others in positive ways? Do you contribute to making your school a great environment for learning?

Do you look professional in your appearance? You don't need to wear a suit but think about the message you are sending by the clothes you choose to wear.

If any of the areas noted above, or other areas of professionalism, are in need of more positive habits, make note of it and add these habits to your weekly work.

Setting Boundaries

Many teachers struggle with setting boundaries. Third-grade teacher Andrea Leach offers the following advice:

This job requires so much energy; we need to conserve what we can to be our best!

You can protect your energy by setting boundaries. This will keep your relationships healthy and help you ask for what you need.

Andrea also shared the following ideas for protecting your energy by setting boundaries in your school and personal life:

- First, identify your personal boundaries by thinking about what makes you the most worried and stressed. Think about how those things could look different with different boundaries.
- Set specific work times every day. Set an alarm to make you go home!
- Set limits for parent communication. Be clear about when you can and cannot be reached and when you can be expected to respond. State your needs. "I can't chat during my prep, how about after school, or give me a call at 4:30."
- Ask for help...seriously!
- Make time to recharge. Pay attention to your body and what it is telling you. Then give your body what it needs! That could include rest, food, water, a night off of thinking about what is overwhelming you, or anything.
- Take breaks...we are not meant to be productive all the time!
- Say NO without any feelings of guilt.
- Pay attention to your teacher friends' boundaries as well.

Setting limits on how our time, energy, and resources are used will help teachers to be happier, healthier, and therefore, more effective in the classroom.

Effective Work Habits

There is no shortage of work to fill your time. One of teachers' biggest challenges is finding time to do everything. Have you built habits connected to maximizing your time?

There are hundreds of articles, books and courses that teach time management and productivity habits. If this is an area of concern for you, you might want to dig deeper. We recommend the books *Atomic Habits* by James Clear and *High-Performance Habits* by Brendan Burchard.

Here are a few time slaying habits we think are especially effective:

Schedule your blocks. Decide ahead of time what you will do in your work blocks, whether they are before school, during a prep time, or after school. You won't always get everything done as planned, but you will avoid having to decide what to do during those periods.

Batch your work. Try to do like tasks together. For example, make a list of phone calls, and try to make them all at the same time. Gather the materials for your next several lessons during the same time block. Don't go to the copier to make copies for next hour, try to plan your copying and do it all at the same time.

Decide how much time something should take. We all know that tasks have a way of expanding to fill the time available. For example, let's say a student asked you to write a college recommendation letter. Decide how much time that should take. 20 minutes? 30 minutes? Set a timer and try to get it done in that amount of time.

Break bigger tasks into small chunks. Teachers don't often have large blocks of time to complete big tasks. Try breaking down a big task into smaller parts. Then you can schedule those smaller pieces into your planning times.

Do the most important tasks first. When you are prioritizing tasks, consider whether there are things that don't really need to be done. Make a game of seeing if you can eliminate some things!

You probably have some good habits, and you probably have some bad habits. We all do. However, altering some of your habits can be a game changer in terms of how you can be more productive and effective, leaving you a little bit less stressed and overwhelmed and giving you more time for things that you want to do in the rest of your life.

Continuous improvement is better than delayed perfection.

Mark Twain

What habits and actions do I have in my life that support me?

What habits and actions do I have in my life that do *not* support me? How might I rethink those habits?

Chapter 6

Build Your Star System

Have you ever watched a teacher movie? You know the ones. A new teacher comes to a school and takes on a class with a history of underperforming. Fighting against all odds, including poverty, racism, or ineffective leadership, our hero teacher works his or her magic and both the teacher and the students succeed beyond anyone's wildest dreams.

We love those movies and find them inspirational. Americans have long loved stories of the underdog who works hard and single-handedly takes on insurmountable challenges only to triumph in the end.

These stories, however, might be as fictional in life as they are in the movies.

Shawn Achor, a former Harvard psychologist, spent years researching how people achieve happiness and success. His research, conducted over a decade with thousands of individuals in countries all over the world, led him to a surprising conclusion.

Individual effort does not account for the most happiness or the best performance.

His conclusion was clear. In his book, *Big Potential,* Achor says:

You can be a superstar; you just can't be one alone.
What you need is a star system: a constellation of positive,
authentic influencers who support each other, reinforce each other,
and make each other better.

Achor, S. (2018). Big potential. New York: Currency. p. 68.

Our biggest growth, our happiness and our success are achieved when we surround ourselves with others who can make us better. In turn, we support others, creating a system where we can all shine more brightly.

If you've ever been part of a winning athletic team, you have experienced this phenomenon. Maybe you've been part of a group that created something amazing such as art, music, or a theatrical performance. You may have been part of a community group that collectively worked to improve your community in impactful ways.

If so, you know the power of working with a star system. Some, but not all, schools have created star systems. So have some, but not all, grade level teams or departments. Some people have star systems in their personal life, but not in their school life. We believe that we need the collective power of a star system in all areas of our lives.

If you are part of a star system, you probably feel it in your bones. You feel supported in your life and in your work. You love your colleagues and know you are better because of them. You are inspired and feel the hum of energy around you. You feel safe to explore and share new ideas. You feel like what you do matters and that you are doing good work.

We all need a star system! If you are not part of a star system currently, it is entirely possible to create your own.

You can choose to create your own star systems and you can choose the people you wish to include. Consider including the following types of people:

Someone to dream with
Dreamers are those who can understand and recognize your vision. They are the ones who help you imagine, plan and dream bigger dreams.

Someone who can mentor you
Mentors are those who have knowledge or skills that you need. They can guide you and inspire you.

Someone who can encourage you
Encouragers are people who cheer you on. They believe in your talents and remind you of them when you feel lost. They will show up for you and celebrate with you.

Someone who can challenge you
Challengers will stretch you. They give you opportunities to discover new ideas or new perspectives. Challengers are the people in your star system who might make you uncomfortable, but they are also often the ones who help you to grow.

Someone who understands your work
Your teacher friends can relate to what you are experiencing. They will laugh with you, cry with you, and engage in "teacher talk" for hours.

Someone who loves you unconditionally
This might be your partner, your family, or a best friend. These are the people you can be most vulnerable with. They are the first people to hear about your wins and the ones you lean on in your worst times. Time with these people nurtures and feeds your soul.

Keep in mind that one person might fulfill separate roles in your life and also that no one person likely fills all the roles.

Also remember that being part of a star system is a reciprocal process. As you have these people in your life, you will also fulfill these roles for other people.

As you are designing your ideal life, make sure that you have a good star system around you. You are going to need others if you want to shine.

Find your teacher people and love them hard.

Teaching is hard and wonderful all at the same time.

No one can do it alone.

Find those people who will cry with you, let you vent,

laugh with you, help turn crazy ideas into a reality,

support you, build you up, and celebrate victories with you and hold them tight.

They are the ones who will tell you that you can do it, even when you don't think you can!

Dani Way-Lawler
High School Special Education Teacher

Who are the members of my star system both at school and in my personal life? How can these people support me? How can we make each other better?

How can I create a supportive star system in my classroom so that students are supported?

Chapter 7

And Now, It's Up to You

The rest of this book is for **your** work. We've designed each question to help you live your life with intention. If you take a few minutes each week to fill in the planning pages, here is what you can expect to happen:

- You will stay close to your dreams, plans and the visions you have for your life.

- You will continually focus on what is most important and remind yourself to get the most important work done first.

- You will be reminded to uncover your unique gifts and talents and to look for opportunities to bring them into the world.

- You will develop your growth mindset as you look for and learn from your success and as you also look for opportunities to incorporate new ideas and strategies into your teaching.

- You will learn to expect challenges, face them head on and deal with your obstacles in a proactive manner.

- You will create and engage with your Star System as you identify support you might need and look for ways to support others.

- Lastly, you will use the habit tracker to identify and focus on habits you want to incorporate into your life.

The work you do is important. So is the life you lead outside of school. You will face many challenges and the negatives can easily overwhelm you. Stress and exhaustion can lead to burn-out. Burn-out can lead to drifting.

We want you to design a life you love. We want you to feel happy, fulfilled and successful both in your personal life and in your school life. We also know that it doesn't happen by chance, but by choice.

Choose to envision the life you want to lead.

Choose to identify your priorities and do the most important things.

Choose to surround yourself with people who can support you.

In our lives and in our work,

one thing we know for sure is that

together, we are always inspired.

Paula and Michele

Weekly Journal

Planning My Week

Date:

What would make me feel joyful or fulfilled this week?

How can I live my best life this week?

What are my three personal priorities for this week?

What are my three work priorities for this week?

What can I do to bring my unique talents and gifts into my life and work this week?

What went well in my teaching last week? How can I build on that success this week?

What new ideas, strategies or supports could I incorporate into my teaching this week?

I would know that this week was a success if my students or I or felt these things:

What obstacles or challenges might I face in my life and work this week?

Who can I connect with this week to help me overcome obstacles or give me support in my life and work?

Who needs me to be my best teacher self this week? What would that support look like?

Keep Track of Your Goals or Habits

Keep track of your eating, exercise, water, sleep, reading, fun, screen time, or any other habits, actions or goals. Give yourself a check mark, rate yourself from 1-10 or even give yourself a letter grade!

Goal/Habit	M	T	W	TH	F	S	S

Teacher Wisdom

"If you want to change the world, it starts in the classroom."

Jenny Adam
Middle School Instrumental Music Teacher

Teachers make a profound impact on the world. At the end of my career, what do I want people to say about me and my impact on the world?

Planning My Week

Date:

What would make me feel joyful or fulfilled this week?

How can I live my best life this week?

What are my three personal priorities for this week?

What are my three work priorities for this week?

What can I do to bring my unique talents and gifts into my life and work this week?

What went well in my teaching last week? How can I build on that success this week?

What new ideas, strategies or supports could I incorporate into my teaching this week?

I would know that this week was a success if my students or I or felt these things:

What obstacles or challenges might I face in my life and work this week?

Who can I connect with this week to help me overcome obstacles or give me support in my life and work?

Who needs me to be my best teacher self this week? What would that support look like?

Keep Track of Your Goals or Habits

Keep track of your eating, exercise, water, sleep, reading, fun, screen time, or any other habits, actions or goals. Give yourself a check mark, rate yourself from 1-10 or even give yourself a letter grade!

Goal/Habit	M	T	W	TH	F	S	S

Teacher Wisdom

"Make sure to make time for yourself and try not to bring work home so you can spend time with those you love."

Cory Reid
Middle and High School Business Teacher

What boundaries do I set for myself about bringing work home? What emotions do I feel when I am working from home? When am I more comfortable bringing work home?

Planning My Week

Date:

What would make me feel joyful or fulfilled this week?

How can I live my best life this week?

What are my three personal priorities for this week?

What are my three work priorities for this week?

What can I do to bring my unique talents and gifts into my life and work this week?

What went well in my teaching last week? How can I build on that success this week?

What new ideas, strategies or supports could I incorporate into my teaching this week?

I would know that this week was a success if my students or I or felt these things:

What obstacles or challenges might I face in my life and work this week?

Who can I connect with this week to help me overcome obstacles or give me support in my life and work?

Who needs me to be my best teacher self this week? What would that support look like?

Keep Track of Your Goals or Habits

Keep track of your eating, exercise, water, sleep, reading, fun, screen time, or any other habits, actions or goals. Give yourself a check mark, rate yourself from 1-10 or even give yourself a letter grade!

Goal/Habit	M	T	W	TH	F	S	S

Teacher Wisdom

"With a child's best interest at heart... you can never go wrong."

Hilary James
4-Year-Old Kindergarten Coordinator

When was the last time I remember *intentionally* making a decision that put a student's best interests at heart? How often do I naturally put a student's best interest at heart *without making a conscience effort* to do so?

Planning My Week

Date:

What would make me feel joyful or fulfilled this week?

How can I live my best life this week?

What are my three personal priorities for this week?

What are my three work priorities for this week?

What can I do to bring my unique talents and gifts into my life and work this week?

What went well in my teaching last week? How can I build on that success this week?

What new ideas, strategies or supports could I incorporate into my teaching this week?

I would know that this week was a success if my students or I or felt these things:

What obstacles or challenges might I face in my life and work this week?

Who can I connect with this week to help me overcome obstacles or give me support in my life and work?

Who needs me to be my best teacher self this week? What would that support look like?

Keep Track of Your Goals or Habits

Keep track of your eating, exercise, water, sleep, reading, fun, screen time, or any other habits, actions or goals. Give yourself a check mark, rate yourself from 1-10 or even give yourself a letter grade!

Goal/Habit	M	T	W	TH	F	S	S

Teacher Wisdom

"Building a relationship with your students will take care of so much 'classroom management' stuff. One of the fastest ways to build that relationship is by admitting and embracing your own mistakes. Students will connect with and respect you so much more once they realize you're a human too."

Hannah Jahn
4th Grade Teacher

When was the last time I made a mistake in front of students? Did I admit to the mistake, embrace it, and make it a learning opportunity? Did I hide it and hope no one noticed? What steps could I take to let students know that I am human too?

Planning My Week

Date:

What would make me feel joyful or fulfilled this week?

How can I live my best life this week?

What are my three personal priorities for this week?

What are my three work priorities for this week?

What can I do to bring my unique talents and gifts into my life and work this week?

What went well in my teaching last week? How can I build on that success this week?

What new ideas, strategies or supports could I incorporate into my teaching this week?

I would know that this week was a success if my students or I or felt these things:

What obstacles or challenges might I face in my life and work this week?

Who can I connect with this week to help me overcome obstacles or give me support in my life and work?

Who needs me to be my best teacher self this week? What would that support look like?

Keep Track of Your Goals or Habits

Keep track of your eating, exercise, water, sleep, reading, fun, screen time, or any other habits, actions or goals. Give yourself a check mark, rate yourself from 1-10 or even give yourself a letter grade!

Goal/Habit	M	T	W	TH	F	S	S

Teacher Wisdom

"Every student matters every day, even on their bad days.
You might be 'the one' who makes a difference in their life
so build relationships, try new things, and do your best.
They are worth it."

Chloe Meisner
PreK-2 School Counselor

When was the last time I was "the one" for a student having a bad day or a series of bad days? How did I build that relationship? In what ways could I replicate those steps with a current student who needs me to be "the one?"

Planning My Week

Date:

What would make me feel joyful or fulfilled this week?

How can I live my best life this week?

What are my three personal priorities for this week?

What are my three work priorities for this week?

What can I do to bring my unique talents and gifts into my life and work this week?

What went well in my teaching last week? How can I build on that success this week?

What new ideas, strategies or supports could I incorporate into my teaching this week?

I would know that this week was a success if my students or I or felt these things:

What obstacles or challenges might I face in my life and work this week?

Who can I connect with this week to help me overcome obstacles or give me support in my life and work?

Who needs me to be my best teacher self this week? What would that support look like?

Keep Track of Your Goals or Habits

Keep track of your eating, exercise, water, sleep, reading, fun, screen time, or any other habits, actions or goals. Give yourself a check mark, rate yourself from 1-10 or even give yourself a letter grade!

Goal/Habit	M	T	W	TH	F	S	S

Teacher Wisdom

"A quote I have hanging, and kids use it all the time, that I feel we all have used this year is, 'It is better to try and fail (learn) than to never try at all.'"

Lisa Zeller
3rd Grade Teacher

When was the last time I let students know it was okay to try, even if failure was the end result? Do I model this? Do I verbalize this? Do I demonstrate this with visuals in my classroom? Is the message to try, even if failure is a result, implicit or explicit in my classroom?

Planning My Week

Date:

What would make me feel joyful or fulfilled this week?

How can I live my best life this week?

What are my three personal priorities for this week?

What are my three work priorities for this week?

What can I do to bring my unique talents and gifts into my life and work this week?

What went well in my teaching last week? How can I build on that success this week?

What new ideas, strategies or supports could I incorporate into my teaching this week?

I would know that this week was a success if my students or I or felt these things:

What obstacles or challenges might I face in my life and work this week?

Who can I connect with this week to help me overcome obstacles or give me support in my life and work?

Who needs me to be my best teacher self this week? What would that support look like?

Keep Track of Your Goals or Habits

Keep track of your eating, exercise, water, sleep, reading, fun, screen time, or any other habits, actions or goals. Give yourself a check mark, rate yourself from 1-10 or even give yourself a letter grade!

Goal/Habit	M	T	W	TH	F	S	S

Teacher Wisdom

"Greet every student every day. 'Good morning. I am glad you are here. You matter.' This sets the tone."

Jennifer Demkier
3rd Grade Teacher

How do I greet students when they enter my classroom? What implicit messages are conveyed through my choice of greetings?

Planning My Week

Date:

What would make me feel joyful or fulfilled this week?

How can I live my best life this week?

What are my three personal priorities for this week?

What are my three work priorities for this week?

What can I do to bring my unique talents and gifts into my life and work this week?

What went well in my teaching last week? How can I build on that success this week?

What new ideas, strategies or supports could I incorporate into my teaching this week?

I would know that this week was a success if my students or I or felt these things:

What obstacles or challenges might I face in my life and work this week?

Who can I connect with this week to help me overcome obstacles or give me support in my life and work?

Who needs me to be my best teacher self this week? What would that support look like?

Keep Track of Your Goals or Habits

Keep track of your eating, exercise, water, sleep, reading, fun, screen time, or any other habits, actions or goals. Give yourself a check mark, rate yourself from 1-10 or even give yourself a letter grade!

Goal/Habit	M	T	W	TH	F	S	S

Teacher Wisdom

"I always remember that my students are someone's everything. I want to be sure I treat ALL of my students with the same respect and compassion I want shown to my own children by their teachers."

Heather Rath
Special Education Teacher

In what ways do I recognize that students have a life (interests, families, friends, talents, etc.) outside of school? How do I help them to realize that I have a life outside of school as well?

Planning My Week

Date:

What would make me feel joyful or fulfilled this week?

How can I live my best life this week?

What are my three personal priorities for this week?

What are my three work priorities for this week?

What can I do to bring my unique talents and gifts into my life and work this week?

What went well in my teaching last week? How can I build on that success this week?

What new ideas, strategies or supports could I incorporate into my teaching this week?

I would know that this week was a success if my students or I or felt these things:

What obstacles or challenges might I face in my life and work this week?

Who can I connect with this week to help me overcome obstacles or give me support in my life and work?

Who needs me to be my best teacher self this week? What would that support look like?

Keep Track of Your Goals or Habits

Keep track of your eating, exercise, water, sleep, reading, fun, screen time, or any other habits, actions or goals. Give yourself a check mark, rate yourself from 1-10 or even give yourself a letter grade!

Goal/Habit	M	T	W	TH	F	S	S

Teacher Wisdom

"We have signs posted in several classrooms around school.

F- first

A-attempt

I-in

L-learning

We tell kids this from kindergarten until 5th grade, all throughout our building."

Kristie Ostrander
Kindergarten Teacher

Consistent messaging is important. What consistent messaging is present in my school? Do I believe in the messaging? In what ways do I contribute to or detract from that consistent messaging?

Planning My Week

Date:

What would make me feel joyful or fulfilled this week?

How can I live my best life this week?

What are my three personal priorities for this week?

What are my three work priorities for this week?

What can I do to bring my unique talents and gifts into my life and work this week?

What went well in my teaching last week? How can I build on that success this week?

What new ideas, strategies or supports could I incorporate into my teaching this week?

I would know that this week was a success if my students or I or felt these things:

What obstacles or challenges might I face in my life and work this week?

Who can I connect with this week to help me overcome obstacles or give me support in my life and work?

Who needs me to be my best teacher self this week? What would that support look like?

Keep Track of Your Goals or Habits

Keep track of your eating, exercise, water, sleep, reading, fun, screen time, or any other habits, actions or goals. Give yourself a check mark, rate yourself from 1-10 or even give yourself a letter grade!

Goal/Habit	M	T	W	TH	F	S	S

Teacher Wisdom

"My advice to new or veteran teachers is that building effective relationships is key to being an effective educator. You need to build relationships with each child so they know you care about them. Students need to know that you are invested in their education. "

Tamara Perushek
Kindergarten teacher

What do I do that shows students that I care about them? How do I show each student that I am invested in them?

Planning My Week

Date:

What would make me feel joyful or fulfilled this week?

How can I live my best life this week?

What are my three personal priorities for this week?

What are my three work priorities for this week?

What can I do to bring my unique talents and gifts into my life and work this week?

What went well in my teaching last week? How can I build on that success this week?

What new ideas, strategies or supports could I incorporate into my teaching this week?

I would know that this week was a success if my students or I or felt these things:

What obstacles or challenges might I face in my life and work this week?

Who can I connect with this week to help me overcome obstacles or give me support in my life and work?

Who needs me to be my best teacher self this week? What would that support look like?

Keep Track of Your Goals or Habits

Keep track of your eating, exercise, water, sleep, reading, fun, screen time, or any other habits, actions or goals. Give yourself a check mark, rate yourself from 1-10 or even give yourself a letter grade!

Goal/Habit	M	T	W	TH	F	S	S

Teacher Wisdom

"I can't remember where I first heard this, but it was many, many years ago. It was the best advice I've ever received.

'Seek first to understand.'"

Kathleen Konrardy
Director of Special Needs

The teacher quoted on this page received meaningful advice that was likely based on the work of Steven Covey. What piece of advice has been the most meaningful to me in my teaching career? Who gave me this advice? When it is most useful?

Planning My Week

Date:

What would make me feel joyful or fulfilled this week?

How can I live my best life this week?

What are my three personal priorities for this week?

What are my three work priorities for this week?

What can I do to bring my unique talents and gifts into my life and work this week?

What went well in my teaching last week? How can I build on that success this week?

What new ideas, strategies or supports could I incorporate into my teaching this week?

I would know that this week was a success if my students or I or felt these things:

What obstacles or challenges might I face in my life and work this week?

Who can I connect with this week to help me overcome obstacles or give me support in my life and work?

Who needs me to be my best teacher self this week? What would that support look like?

Keep Track of Your Goals or Habits

Keep track of your eating, exercise, water, sleep, reading, fun, screen time, or any other habits, actions or goals. Give yourself a check mark, rate yourself from 1-10 or even give yourself a letter grade!

Goal/Habit	M	T	W	TH	F	S	S

Teacher Wisdom

"Students need to remember that teachers are people too, so tell that bad joke, admit when you are wrong, share your passions, laugh when something out of the ordinary happens in the classroom, and just be yourself. Quite often, the 'true you' teacher is exactly who someone needed."

Andy Bishop
High School English and Math Teacher

When was the last time I laughed with my students? What were the circumstances that led to the laughter? To what degree am I content with the amount of laughter generated in my classroom?

Planning My Week

Date:

What would make me feel joyful or fulfilled this week?

How can I live my best life this week?

What are my three personal priorities for this week?

What are my three work priorities for this week?

What can I do to bring my unique talents and gifts into my life and work this week?

What went well in my teaching last week? How can I build on that success this week?

What new ideas, strategies or supports could I incorporate into my teaching this week?

I would know that this week was a success if my students or I or felt these things:

What obstacles or challenges might I face in my life and work this week?

Who can I connect with this week to help me overcome obstacles or give me support in my life and work?

Who needs me to be my best teacher self this week? What would that support look like?

Keep Track of Your Goals or Habits

Keep track of your eating, exercise, water, sleep, reading, fun, screen time, or any other habits, actions or goals. Give yourself a check mark, rate yourself from 1-10 or even give yourself a letter grade!

Goal/Habit	M	T	W	TH	F	S	S

Teacher Wisdom

"YOU set the tone. Make it a good one."

Kendra Starkey
Special Education Teacher

What is the tone I set in my classroom? What is the tone I set in my home? How are the tones I set in these two environments the same? How are they different? What changes, if any, would I like to make to the tone of my home and/or my classroom?

Planning My Week

Date:

What would make me feel joyful or fulfilled this week?

How can I live my best life this week?

What are my three personal priorities for this week?

What are my three work priorities for this week?

What can I do to bring my unique talents and gifts into my life and work this week?

What went well in my teaching last week? How can I build on that success this week?

What new ideas, strategies or supports could I incorporate into my teaching this week?

I would know that this week was a success if my students or I or felt these things:

What obstacles or challenges might I face in my life and work this week?

Who can I connect with this week to help me overcome obstacles or give me support in my life and work?

Who needs me to be my best teacher self this week? What would that support look like?

Keep Track of Your Goals or Habits

Keep track of your eating, exercise, water, sleep, reading, fun, screen time, or any other habits, actions or goals. Give yourself a check mark, rate yourself from 1-10 or even give yourself a letter grade!

Goal/Habit	M	T	W	TH	F	S	S

Teacher Wisdom

"I have 3 quotes I use frequently:

Are you a problem starter or problem solver?

Teamwork makes the dream work!

Pick flowers, not fights."

Erin Diekman
4th Grade Teacher

What are the top 2-3 quotes I use most frequently with my students?
In what ways do the quotes I say to my students impact their actions?
In what ways do these quotes have meaning in my own life?

Planning My Week

Date:

What would make me feel joyful or fulfilled this week?

How can I live my best life this week?

What are my three personal priorities for this week?

What are my three work priorities for this week?

What can I do to bring my unique talents and gifts into my life and work this week?

What went well in my teaching last week? How can I build on that success this week?

What new ideas, strategies or supports could I incorporate into my teaching this week?

I would know that this week was a success if my students or I or felt these things:

What obstacles or challenges might I face in my life and work this week?

Who can I connect with this week to help me overcome obstacles or give me support in my life and work?

Who needs me to be my best teacher self this week? What would that support look like?

Keep Track of Your Goals or Habits

Keep track of your eating, exercise, water, sleep, reading, fun, screen time, or any other habits, actions or goals. Give yourself a check mark, rate yourself from 1-10 or even give yourself a letter grade!

Goal/Habit	M	T	W	TH	F	S	S

Teacher Wisdom

"When students tell me I'm really good at something, I tell them, "I've been practicing since I was 4. It was hard then, but now it's easy.'"

Julie Voss
Pre-K Teacher

What is the last thing I learned that took me more practice than I had originally anticipated? What did I learn from all that practice? What are the lessons I learned from this experience that I can pass on to my students?

Planning My Week

Date:

What would make me feel joyful or fulfilled this week?

How can I live my best life this week?

What are my three personal priorities for this week?

What are my three work priorities for this week?

What can I do to bring my unique talents and gifts into my life and work this week?

What went well in my teaching last week? How can I build on that success this week?

What new ideas, strategies or supports could I incorporate into my teaching this week?

I would know that this week was a success if my students or I or felt these things:

What obstacles or challenges might I face in my life and work this week?

Who can I connect with this week to help me overcome obstacles or give me support in my life and work?

Who needs me to be my best teacher self this week? What would that support look like?

Keep Track of Your Goals or Habits

Keep track of your eating, exercise, water, sleep, reading, fun, screen time, or any other habits, actions or goals. Give yourself a check mark, rate yourself from 1-10 or even give yourself a letter grade!

Goal/Habit	M	T	W	TH	F	S	S

Teacher Wisdom

"Listening and caring about a student's passion shows them that you see them as more than just their grade. It goes a long way in building strong relationships and a solid classroom culture."

K'Lynn Lawler
High School Spanish Teacher

When was the last time I was able to sit down and *really listen* to someone at home or at work? How did the conversation go? When listening, did I truly listen without judgement? How did the other person feel when the conversation was complete? How did I feel?

Planning My Week

Date:

What would make me feel joyful or fulfilled this week?

How can I live my best life this week?

What are my three personal priorities for this week?

What are my three work priorities for this week?

What can I do to bring my unique talents and gifts into my life and work this week?

What went well in my teaching last week? How can I build on that success this week?

What new ideas, strategies or supports could I incorporate into my teaching this week?

I would know that this week was a success if my students or I or felt these things:

What obstacles or challenges might I face in my life and work this week?

Who can I connect with this week to help me overcome obstacles or give me support in my life and work?

Who needs me to be my best teacher self this week? What would that support look like?

Keep Track of Your Goals or Habits

Keep track of your eating, exercise, water, sleep, reading, fun, screen time, or any other habits, actions or goals. Give yourself a check mark, rate yourself from 1-10 or even give yourself a letter grade!

Goal/Habit	M	T	W	TH	F	S	S

Teacher Wisdom

"In a world full of chaos and fear, make your classroom a space filled with safety and acceptance. Make it a place where students can feel free to express themselves and explore their identity."

Molly Heil
High School Theatre Teacher

What opportunities do students have to express themselves and their individuality in my classroom? How do my students take advantage of opportunities I provide for them to embrace their identities in my classroom?

Planning My Week

Date:

What would make me feel joyful or fulfilled this week?

How can I live my best life this week?

What are my three personal priorities for this week?

What are my three work priorities for this week?

What can I do to bring my unique talents and gifts into my life and work this week?

What went well in my teaching last week? How can I build on that success this week?

What new ideas, strategies or supports could I incorporate into my teaching this week?

I would know that this week was a success if my students or I or felt these things:

What obstacles or challenges might I face in my life and work this week?

Who can I connect with this week to help me overcome obstacles or give me support in my life and work?

Who needs me to be my best teacher self this week? What would that support look like?

Keep Track of Your Goals or Habits

Keep track of your eating, exercise, water, sleep, reading, fun, screen time, or any other habits, actions or goals. Give yourself a check mark, rate yourself from 1-10 or even give yourself a letter grade!

Goal/Habit	M	T	W	TH	F	S	S

Teacher Wisdom

"Kids that have all of their needs met at home come to school to learn but not all kids get their needs met at home. Sometimes meeting the human needs of your students comes before the content lesson, and that's ok! The content will come when the students feel loved, connected with, cared for, and safe."

Katie Overstreet
5th/6th Grade Special Education and Co-Taught Literacy Teacher

When was the last time that I set content aside to address the human needs of a student or students? What were the consequences of that decision? Would I make the same decision if I were in that situation again? Why or why not?

Planning My Week

Date:

What would make me feel joyful or fulfilled this week?

How can I live my best life this week?

What are my three personal priorities for this week?

What are my three work priorities for this week?

What can I do to bring my unique talents and gifts into my life and work this week?

What went well in my teaching last week? How can I build on that success this week?

What new ideas, strategies or supports could I incorporate into my teaching this week?

I would know that this week was a success if my students or I or felt these things:

What obstacles or challenges might I face in my life and work this week?

Who can I connect with this week to help me overcome obstacles or give me support in my life and work?

Who needs me to be my best teacher self this week? What would that support look like?

Keep Track of Your Goals or Habits

Keep track of your eating, exercise, water, sleep, reading, fun, screen time, or any other habits, actions or goals. Give yourself a check mark, rate yourself from 1-10 or even give yourself a letter grade!

Goal/Habit	M	T	W	TH	F	S	S

Teacher Wisdom

"Every child deserves my best every day in every way."

Jennifer Flores
Special Education Coach

What does my best teacher-self look like? Sound like? Feel like? How can I bring more of my best teacher-self into the classroom each day?

Planning My Week

Date:

What would make me feel joyful or fulfilled this week?

How can I live my best life this week?

What are my three personal priorities for this week?

What are my three work priorities for this week?

What can I do to bring my unique talents and gifts into my life and work this week?

What went well in my teaching last week? How can I build on that success this week?

What new ideas, strategies or supports could I incorporate into my teaching this week?

I would know that this week was a success if my students or I or felt these things:

What obstacles or challenges might I face in my life and work this week?

Who can I connect with this week to help me overcome obstacles or give me support in my life and work?

Who needs me to be my best teacher self this week? What would that support look like?

Keep Track of Your Goals or Habits

Keep track of your eating, exercise, water, sleep, reading, fun, screen time, or any other habits, actions or goals. Give yourself a check mark, rate yourself from 1-10 or even give yourself a letter grade!

Goal/Habit	M	T	W	TH	F	S	S

Teacher Wisdom

"I have high expectations for students. I count on them as leaders and role models for others, older and younger. I believe in them and have them rise to the occasion. I teach them to believe in the Power of Yet, and positive self-talk. Sometimes you have to close the book and teach from your head and heart."

Kristal Schaul
5th Grade Teacher

Having high expectations for students should always include showing them that you believe in them while allowing them to grow. How have I set high expectations and then supported students in achieving those expectations?

Planning My Week

Date:

What would make me feel joyful or fulfilled this week?

How can I live my best life this week?

What are my three personal priorities for this week?

What are my three work priorities for this week?

What can I do to bring my unique talents and gifts into my life and work this week?

What went well in my teaching last week? How can I build on that success this week?

What new ideas, strategies or supports could I incorporate into my teaching this week?

I would know that this week was a success if my students or I or felt these things:

What obstacles or challenges might I face in my life and work this week?

Who can I connect with this week to help me overcome obstacles or give me support in my life and work?

Who needs me to be my best teacher self this week? What would that support look like?

Keep Track of Your Goals or Habits

Keep track of your eating, exercise, water, sleep, reading, fun, screen time, or any other habits, actions or goals. Give yourself a check mark, rate yourself from 1-10 or even give yourself a letter grade!

Goal/Habit	M	T	W	TH	F	S	S

Teacher Wisdom

"Every child deserves a champion, so be the teacher you needed."

JoAnne Williamson
Former K-12 Teacher, Current College Instructor, and Teacher Candidate Supervisor

When was the last time I advocated for a student? Why did I feel compelled to advocate in that particular situation? What were the positive and negative consequences of my advocacy? What changes would I make, if any, to the ways in which I advocated for that student?

Planning My Week

Date:

What would make me feel joyful or fulfilled this week?

How can I live my best life this week?

What are my three personal priorities for this week?

What are my three work priorities for this week?

What can I do to bring my unique talents and gifts into my life and work this week?

What went well in my teaching last week? How can I build on that success this week?

What new ideas, strategies or supports could I incorporate into my teaching this week?

I would know that this week was a success if my students or I or felt these things:

What obstacles or challenges might I face in my life and work this week?

Who can I connect with this week to help me overcome obstacles or give me support in my life and work?

Who needs me to be my best teacher self this week? What would that support look like?

Keep Track of Your Goals or Habits

Keep track of your eating, exercise, water, sleep, reading, fun, screen time, or any other habits, actions or goals. Give yourself a check mark, rate yourself from 1-10 or even give yourself a letter grade!

Goal/Habit	M	T	W	TH	F	S	S

Teacher Wisdom

"I heard this from my first boss but continue to preach this concept. 'Nobody is perfect. Practice makes progress.'"

Tina House
Special Education Teacher

It is crucial to have and model a growth mindset. What is something I have been trying to do better? What steps have I taken to improve in this area? How can I tell that I am making progress?

Planning My Week

Date:

What would make me feel joyful or fulfilled this week?

How can I live my best life this week?

What are my three personal priorities for this week?

What are my three work priorities for this week?

What can I do to bring my unique talents and gifts into my life and work this week?

What went well in my teaching last week? How can I build on that success this week?

What new ideas, strategies or supports could I incorporate into my teaching this week?

I would know that this week was a success if my students or I or felt these things:

What obstacles or challenges might I face in my life and work this week?

Who can I connect with this week to help me overcome obstacles or give me support in my life and work?

Who needs me to be my best teacher self this week? What would that support look like?

Keep Track of Your Goals or Habits

Keep track of your eating, exercise, water, sleep, reading, fun, screen time, or any other habits, actions or goals. Give yourself a check mark, rate yourself from 1-10 or even give yourself a letter grade!

Goal/Habit	M	T	W	TH	F	S	S

Teacher Wisdom

"The greatest relationship building conversation I ever had with a student was mostly a one-way conversation. I said three words in it. 'What's going on?'"

Lee Johnson
Strategist Teacher Leader/Special Educator K-12

Relationship building is not always easy, but it is always important. Who was the last person with whom I had a relationship building conversation? How was this conversation important in building or enhancing our relationship? In what ways did my interactions with this person change after this conversation?

Planning My Week

Date:

What would make me feel joyful or fulfilled this week?

How can I live my best life this week?

What are my three personal priorities for this week?

What are my three work priorities for this week?

What can I do to bring my unique talents and gifts into my life and work this week?

What went well in my teaching last week? How can I build on that success this week?

What new ideas, strategies or supports could I incorporate into my teaching this week?

I would know that this week was a success if my students or I or felt these things:

What obstacles or challenges might I face in my life and work this week?

Who can I connect with this week to help me overcome obstacles or give me support in my life and work?

Who needs me to be my best teacher self this week? What would that support look like?

Keep Track of Your Goals or Habits

Keep track of your eating, exercise, water, sleep, reading, fun, screen time, or any other habits, actions or goals. Give yourself a check mark, rate yourself from 1-10 or even give yourself a letter grade!

Goal/Habit	M	T	W	TH	F	S	S

Teacher Wisdom

"Love is the most important element of teaching. When we look with eyes of love, we will empower students, solve problems, and find joy in teaching. The root of being successful is that every student knows they are loved- even on their 'bad days' or when they don't know the answer. Love is the most powerful thing you could ever teach someone."

Brooke Chapman
Elementary Special Education Teacher

Teaching love can be powerful. Giving and receiving love is easier with some people than with others. When I am giving and receiving love, what does it look and feel like? In contrast, when I don't feel as if I am giving or receiving love, what does it look and feel like? How do others notice and react to my actions?

Planning My Week

Date:

What would make me feel joyful or fulfilled this week?

How can I live my best life this week?

What are my three personal priorities for this week?

What are my three work priorities for this week?

What can I do to bring my unique talents and gifts into my life and work this week?

What went well in my teaching last week? How can I build on that success this week?

What new ideas, strategies or supports could I incorporate into my teaching this week?

I would know that this week was a success if my students or I or felt these things:

What obstacles or challenges might I face in my life and work this week?

Who can I connect with this week to help me overcome obstacles or give me support in my life and work?

Who needs me to be my best teacher self this week? What would that support look like?

Keep Track of Your Goals or Habits

Keep track of your eating, exercise, water, sleep, reading, fun, screen time, or any other habits, actions or goals. Give yourself a check mark, rate yourself from 1-10 or even give yourself a letter grade!

Goal/Habit	M	T	W	TH	F	S	S

Teacher Wisdom

"Teaching is not a solo sport. It's a team sport. You cannot do this alone. Find your team of colleagues. Lean on them for support. Ask for help when needed. Help them when you can. And be sure to celebrate each other's successes."

Jenny Forbes
Elementary Special Education Teacher

When was the last time I asked for help from a colleague? What did I gain from the advice or support given to me? When did I offer support to a colleague?

Planning My Week

Date:

What would make me feel joyful or fulfilled this week?

How can I live my best life this week?

What are my three personal priorities for this week?

What are my three work priorities for this week?

What can I do to bring my unique talents and gifts into my life and work this week?

What went well in my teaching last week? How can I build on that success this week?

What new ideas, strategies or supports could I incorporate into my teaching this week?

I would know that this week was a success if my students or I or felt these things:

What obstacles or challenges might I face in my life and work this week?

Who can I connect with this week to help me overcome obstacles or give me support in my life and work?

Who needs me to be my best teacher self this week? What would that support look like?

Keep Track of Your Goals or Habits

Keep track of your eating, exercise, water, sleep, reading, fun, screen time, or any other habits, actions or goals. Give yourself a check mark, rate yourself from 1-10 or even give yourself a letter grade!

Goal/Habit	M	T	W	TH	F	S	S

Teacher Wisdom

"Make sure every person entering your room leaves with their dignity."

Roy Hansen
Retired Elementary Teacher, Principal, and Teacher Education Instructor

How do I allow students and others to maintain their dignity? How does this affect their relationship with me and their relationship with others?

Planning My Week

Date:

What would make me feel joyful or fulfilled this week?

How can I live my best life this week?

What are my three personal priorities for this week?

What are my three work priorities for this week?

What can I do to bring my unique talents and gifts into my life and work this week?

What went well in my teaching last week? How can I build on that success this week?

What new ideas, strategies or supports could I incorporate into my teaching this week?

I would know that this week was a success if my students or I or felt these things:

What obstacles or challenges might I face in my life and work this week?

Who can I connect with this week to help me overcome obstacles or give me support in my life and work?

Who needs me to be my best teacher self this week? What would that support look like?

Keep Track of Your Goals or Habits

Keep track of your eating, exercise, water, sleep, reading, fun, screen time, or any other habits, actions or goals. Give yourself a check mark, rate yourself from 1-10 or even give yourself a letter grade!

Goal/Habit	M	T	W	TH	F	S	S

Teacher Wisdom

"Use passion to drive learning
and learning will become a passion."

Crystal Flaherty
3rd Grade

How can I fuel my teaching with passion so my students will become passionate learners?

Planning My Week

Date:

What would make me feel joyful or fulfilled this week?

How can I live my best life this week?

What are my three personal priorities for this week?

What are my three work priorities for this week?

What can I do to bring my unique talents and gifts into my life and work this week?

What went well in my teaching last week? How can I build on that success this week?

What new ideas, strategies or supports could I incorporate into my teaching this week?

I would know that this week was a success if my students or I or felt these things:

What obstacles or challenges might I face in my life and work this week?

Who can I connect with this week to help me overcome obstacles or give me support in my life and work?

Who needs me to be my best teacher self this week? What would that support look like?

Keep Track of Your Goals or Habits

Keep track of your eating, exercise, water, sleep, reading, fun, screen time, or any other habits, actions or goals. Give yourself a check mark, rate yourself from 1-10 or even give yourself a letter grade!

Goal/Habit	M	T	W	TH	F	S	S

Teacher Wisdom

"You may be the only one they have that teaches them how be a problem solver. Take the opportunity to do it. Far too many times, as educators, we feel the need to help, to jump in to make something right or help the struggling student. Most times, it's completely acceptable, but at times, take the opportunity to teach them how to work through a problem...Don't be quick to answer, instead make it a problem solving, teachable moment."

Kate Laskowski
3rd Grade Teacher

What do I do that encourages students to solve their own problems? If students solved, or at least attempted to solve more problems on their own before coming to me, which projects or tasks could benefit from the additional time?

Planning My Week

Date:

What would make me feel joyful or fulfilled this week?

How can I live my best life this week?

What are my three personal priorities for this week?

What are my three work priorities for this week?

What can I do to bring my unique talents and gifts into my life and work this week?

What went well in my teaching last week? How can I build on that success this week?

What new ideas, strategies or supports could I incorporate into my teaching this week?

I would know that this week was a success if my students or I or felt these things:

What obstacles or challenges might I face in my life and work this week?

Who can I connect with this week to help me overcome obstacles or give me support in my life and work?

Who needs me to be my best teacher self this week? What would that support look like?

Keep Track of Your Goals or Habits

Keep track of your eating, exercise, water, sleep, reading, fun, screen time, or any other habits, actions or goals. Give yourself a check mark, rate yourself from 1-10 or even give yourself a letter grade!

Goal/Habit	M	T	W	TH	F	S	S

Teacher Wisdom

"Everyone wants learning to be fun, the more engaged you are the more engaging it will be!"

Steffany King
High School Art Teacher

What was the last highly engaging lesson I planned? What did I learn from that lesson that I can apply to future planning?

Planning My Week

Date:

What would make me feel joyful or fulfilled this week?

How can I live my best life this week?

What are my three personal priorities for this week?

What are my three work priorities for this week?

What can I do to bring my unique talents and gifts into my life and work this week?

What went well in my teaching last week? How can I build on that success this week?

What new ideas, strategies or supports could I incorporate into my teaching this week?

I would know that this week was a success if my students or I or felt these things:

What obstacles or challenges might I face in my life and work this week?

Who can I connect with this week to help me overcome obstacles or give me support in my life and work?

Who needs me to be my best teacher self this week? What would that support look like?

Keep Track of Your Goals or Habits

Keep track of your eating, exercise, water, sleep, reading, fun, screen time, or any other habits, actions or goals. Give yourself a check mark, rate yourself from 1-10 or even give yourself a letter grade!

Goal/Habit	M	T	W	TH	F	S	S

Teacher Wisdom

"You are right where you are meant to be."

Katie Bormann
1st Year Kindergarten Teacher, School Counselor, and Former High School
Spanish Teacher

Life's journey is unpredictable. How do I know that I am right where I am supposed to be? How can I tell if this is where I am meant to stay or if this is just a stopping point along my journey?

Planning My Week

Date:

What would make me feel joyful or fulfilled this week?

How can I live my best life this week?

What are my three personal priorities for this week?

What are my three work priorities for this week?

What can I do to bring my unique talents and gifts into my life and work this week?

What went well in my teaching last week? How can I build on that success this week?

What new ideas, strategies or supports could I incorporate into my teaching this week?

I would know that this week was a success if my students or I or felt these things:

What obstacles or challenges might I face in my life and work this week?

Who can I connect with this week to help me overcome obstacles or give me support in my life and work?

Who needs me to be my best teacher self this week? What would that support look like?

Keep Track of Your Goals or Habits

Keep track of your eating, exercise, water, sleep, reading, fun, screen time, or any other habits, actions or goals. Give yourself a check mark, rate yourself from 1-10 or even give yourself a letter grade!

Goal/Habit	M	T	W	TH	F	S	S

Teacher Wisdom

"What you know today doesn't make yesterday wrong, it makes today better."

Dan Wendler
Elementary School Principal

Like our students, we are always learning and growing. What is something I have learned in the last few weeks that will make me better going forward?

Planning My Week

Date:

What would make me feel joyful or fulfilled this week?

How can I live my best life this week?

What are my three personal priorities for this week?

What are my three work priorities for this week?

What can I do to bring my unique talents and gifts into my life and work this week?

What went well in my teaching last week? How can I build on that success this week?

What new ideas, strategies or supports could I incorporate into my teaching this week?

I would know that this week was a success if my students or I or felt these things:

What obstacles or challenges might I face in my life and work this week?

Who can I connect with this week to help me overcome obstacles or give me support in my life and work?

Who needs me to be my best teacher self this week? What would that support look like?

Keep Track of Your Goals or Habits

Keep track of your eating, exercise, water, sleep, reading, fun, screen time, or any other habits, actions or goals. Give yourself a check mark, rate yourself from 1-10 or even give yourself a letter grade!

Goal/Habit	M	T	W	TH	F	S	S

Teacher Wisdom

"Joke."

Heather Riley
High School Wellness Teacher

Do I incorporate jokes into my teaching or classroom environment? How could I add more jokes to my repertoire as a means to lighten the mood and to make my students smile and laugh?

Planning My Week

Date:

What would make me feel joyful or fulfilled this week?

How can I live my best life this week?

What are my three personal priorities for this week?

What are my three work priorities for this week?

What can I do to bring my unique talents and gifts into my life and work this week?

What went well in my teaching last week? How can I build on that success this week?

What new ideas, strategies or supports could I incorporate into my teaching this week?

I would know that this week was a success if my students or I or felt these things:

What obstacles or challenges might I face in my life and work this week?

Who can I connect with this week to help me overcome obstacles or give me support in my life and work?

Who needs me to be my best teacher self this week? What would that support look like?

Keep Track of Your Goals or Habits

Keep track of your eating, exercise, water, sleep, reading, fun, screen time, or any other habits, actions or goals. Give yourself a check mark, rate yourself from 1-10 or even give yourself a letter grade!

Goal/Habit	M	T	W	TH	F	S	S

Teacher Wisdom

"You don't have to be like everyone else at your school.
Life with only bags of yellow Starburst would stink.
Don't be afraid to be your true unicorn self."

Colin Rust
4th Grade Teacher

How do I embrace what makes me unique as a teacher? In what ways
do I celebrate the unique gifts I bring to my students and my school?

Planning My Week

Date:

What would make me feel joyful or fulfilled this week?

How can I live my best life this week?

What are my three personal priorities for this week?

What are my three work priorities for this week?

What can I do to bring my unique talents and gifts into my life and work this week?

What went well in my teaching last week? How can I build on that success this week?

What new ideas, strategies or supports could I incorporate into my teaching this week?

I would know that this week was a success if my students or I or felt these things:

What obstacles or challenges might I face in my life and work this week?

Who can I connect with this week to help me overcome obstacles or give me support in my life and work?

Who needs me to be my best teacher self this week? What would that support look like?

Keep Track of Your Goals or Habits

Keep track of your eating, exercise, water, sleep, reading, fun, screen time, or any other habits, actions or goals. Give yourself a check mark, rate yourself from 1-10 or even give yourself a letter grade!

Goal/Habit	M	T	W	TH	F	S	S

Teacher Wisdom

"Every student has a story they want to tell, so let that voice be heard. Some days hearing their story is just as important as getting through the curriculum."

Kelsey Kilburg
High School Math Teacher

What opportunities do I give students to let their voice be heard? How do I make sure students are aware that their voice is important, whether I agree with their opinions or not?

Planning My Week

Date:

What would make me feel joyful or fulfilled this week?

How can I live my best life this week?

What are my three personal priorities for this week?

What are my three work priorities for this week?

What can I do to bring my unique talents and gifts into my life and work this week?

What went well in my teaching last week? How can I build on that success this week?

What new ideas, strategies or supports could I incorporate into my teaching this week?

I would know that this week was a success if my students or I or felt these things:

What obstacles or challenges might I face in my life and work this week?

Who can I connect with this week to help me overcome obstacles or give me support in my life and work?

Who needs me to be my best teacher self this week? What would that support look like?

Keep Track of Your Goals or Habits

Keep track of your eating, exercise, water, sleep, reading, fun, screen time, or any other habits, actions or goals. Give yourself a check mark, rate yourself from 1-10 or even give yourself a letter grade!

Goal/Habit	M	T	W	TH	F	S	S

Teacher Wisdom

"Take time to teach leadership skills every day. One of the most rewarding things to hear from a player or student is, 'That's not how we do things here, but let me help you.'"

Travis Ferrell
7th Grade Math Teacher and Varsity Boys Basketball Coach

What opportunities do I give students to practice leadership skills in a safe and supportive manner? Which of my students have untapped leadership potential? How can I help foster their unique leadership skills?

Planning My Week

Date:

What would make me feel joyful or fulfilled this week?

How can I live my best life this week?

What are my three personal priorities for this week?

What are my three work priorities for this week?

What can I do to bring my unique talents and gifts into my life and work this week?

What went well in my teaching last week? How can I build on that success this week?

What new ideas, strategies or supports could I incorporate into my teaching this week?

I would know that this week was a success if my students or I or felt these things:

What obstacles or challenges might I face in my life and work this week?

Who can I connect with this week to help me overcome obstacles or give me support in my life and work?

Who needs me to be my best teacher self this week? What would that support look like?

Keep Track of Your Goals or Habits

Keep track of your eating, exercise, water, sleep, reading, fun, screen time, or any other habits, actions or goals. Give yourself a check mark, rate yourself from 1-10 or even give yourself a letter grade!

Goal/Habit	M	T	W	TH	F	S	S

Teacher Wisdom

"My grandma, who was a fabulous teacher, would say, 'The mind can only take in what the seat can endure!' She knew, even in the late 40's and 50's, kids need movement while learning."

Kristi Alvarado
Special Education Teacher

Sometimes movement is connected to learning and other times movement is built into a school day as a sensory release. In what ways do I incorporate movement into my classroom? Is the movement in my classroom connected to learning, more for a sensory break, or a combination of the two?

Planning My Week

Date:

What would make me feel joyful or fulfilled this week?

How can I live my best life this week?

What are my three personal priorities for this week?

What are my three work priorities for this week?

What can I do to bring my unique talents and gifts into my life and work this week?

What went well in my teaching last week? How can I build on that success this week?

What new ideas, strategies or supports could I incorporate into my teaching this week?

I would know that this week was a success if my students or I or felt these things:

What obstacles or challenges might I face in my life and work this week?

Who can I connect with this week to help me overcome obstacles or give me support in my life and work?

Who needs me to be my best teacher self this week? What would that support look like?

Keep Track of Your Goals or Habits

Keep track of your eating, exercise, water, sleep, reading, fun, screen time, or any other habits, actions or goals. Give yourself a check mark, rate yourself from 1-10 or even give yourself a letter grade!

Goal/Habit	M	T	W	TH	F	S	S

Teacher Wisdom

"Find something you love about every child. Build relationships first."

Stephanie Bell
5th Grade International Baccalaureate Primary Years Program
Exhibition Teacher

Is there a student I am struggling to connect with? What steps can I take to find something I love about this student? How could this help our relationship?

Planning My Week

Date:

What would make me feel joyful or fulfilled this week?

How can I live my best life this week?

What are my three personal priorities for this week?

What are my three work priorities for this week?

What can I do to bring my unique talents and gifts into my life and work this week?

What went well in my teaching last week? How can I build on that success this week?

What new ideas, strategies or supports could I incorporate into my teaching this week?

I would know that this week was a success if my students or I or felt these things:

What obstacles or challenges might I face in my life and work this week?

Who can I connect with this week to help me overcome obstacles or give me support in my life and work?

Who needs me to be my best teacher self this week? What would that support look like?

Keep Track of Your Goals or Habits

Keep track of your eating, exercise, water, sleep, reading, fun, screen time, or any other habits, actions or goals. Give yourself a check mark, rate yourself from 1-10 or even give yourself a letter grade!

Goal/Habit	M	T	W	TH	F	S	S

Teacher Wisdom

"To be the best teacher I can be, I've realized the importance of continuing my own learning outside of the classroom. No, I'm not talking about professional development, although that's quite important. This year, I taught myself how to play tennis, how to plant lavender, and how to cook lemons from the tree next door. Bringing out the student in myself helps me to better understand the struggle and joy in obtaining a new skill, no matter how small. These little achievements bring me a sense of renewal and also help me to better identify with the struggles and successes of my own students."

Elizabeth Drewelow
Reading Specialist

What is something I would like to learn in the upcoming months? How can I continually remind myself that learning is a process, so I don't give up when I struggle to master this new skill or hobby?

Planning My Week

Date:

What would make me feel joyful or fulfilled this week?

How can I live my best life this week?

What are my three personal priorities for this week?

What are my three work priorities for this week?

What can I do to bring my unique talents and gifts into my life and work this week?

What went well in my teaching last week? How can I build on that success this week?

What new ideas, strategies or supports could I incorporate into my teaching this week?

I would know that this week was a success if my students or I or felt these things:

What obstacles or challenges might I face in my life and work this week?

Who can I connect with this week to help me overcome obstacles or give me support in my life and work?

Who needs me to be my best teacher self this week? What would that support look like?

Keep Track of Your Goals or Habits

Keep track of your eating, exercise, water, sleep, reading, fun, screen time, or any other habits, actions or goals. Give yourself a check mark, rate yourself from 1-10 or even give yourself a letter grade!

Goal/Habit	M	T	W	TH	F	S	S

Teacher Wisdom

"Be the teacher that is willing to think outside of the box. Sometimes, following the prescribed curriculum is NOT what is best for your students. Find what interests the students and they will be engaged, interested, and learn more! Push them to succeed and they will always step up!"

Molly Browning
5th Grade Talented and Gifted Reading Teacher

How do I take the prescribed curriculum, think outside the box, and make it better? How do my students react to the extra effort I put in to engage and interest them?

Planning My Week

Date:

What would make me feel joyful or fulfilled this week?

How can I live my best life this week?

What are my three personal priorities for this week?

What are my three work priorities for this week?

What can I do to bring my unique talents and gifts into my life and work this week?

What went well in my teaching last week? How can I build on that success this week?

What new ideas, strategies or supports could I incorporate into my teaching this week?

I would know that this week was a success if my students or I or felt these things:

What obstacles or challenges might I face in my life and work this week?

Who can I connect with this week to help me overcome obstacles or give me support in my life and work?

Who needs me to be my best teacher self this week? What would that support look like?

Keep Track of Your Goals or Habits

Keep track of your eating, exercise, water, sleep, reading, fun, screen time, or any other habits, actions or goals. Give yourself a check mark, rate yourself from 1-10 or even give yourself a letter grade!

Goal/Habit	M	T	W	TH	F	S	S

Teacher Wisdom

"Because the best advice is found inside a Dove chocolate wrapper... 'Be fearlessly authentic.' And if you are considering going into leadership or administration, my correlated advice would be 'Buy the expensive chocolate.'"

Rebecca Fabricius
Director of Clinical Education, Former K-12 Teacher

How do I embrace my authentic self at work? How do I embrace my authentic self in my personal life? How would others identify that I am authentically myself?

Teacher Wisdom

"When students look back and think about me as their teacher, I don't want them to think about me as a teacher who taught them how to read or write, I want them to think of me as a teacher who really cared about them."

Joyce Meier Guimond
Former teacher and college instructor, Minister

If I had to sum up my teacher impact in one sentence, what would I say? How would I like to be known and remembered?

About the Authors

Paula Schmidt and Michele Vosberg are award winning educators who have worked with thousands of teachers and schools from around the world. They are key people in each other's Star System!

Paula Schmidt is an energetic and passionate educator. Paula's gift is seeing the strengths and potential in people and situations, a skill she uses daily in all aspects of her life. She is energized by thinking out-of-the box and enthusiastically challenges others to do the same.

Paula holds a bachelor's degree in Elementary and Special Education from Winona State University, a master's degree with an emphasis on Students-At-Risk from Marian College, and an Ed.D. in Special Education/Inclusive Leadership from The University of Northern Iowa.

Paula lives in Dubuque, Iowa with her husband and three children. She loves traveling, reading, and meeting new people. When she is not working, you can find her attending her children's many activities or sitting on the deck relaxing with her family or friends.

Michele Vosberg is a life-long educator, international speaker, and author. She has taught students at every grade and level from preschool through graduate school. Michele loves to learn and share ideas by synthesizing them and making them easy to understand. She also sees potential and loves bringing potential to life. Michele uses her gifts to help others discover and bring about their own best gifts.

Michele holds a B.S. in Elementary Education from the University of Wisconsin, Madison, a Master of Science degree from UW Madison in Curriculum and Instruction, and a Ph.D. in Education from Capella University.

Michele lives in Madison, Wisconsin with her husband and two cats. She also has two grown daughters. When she is not working, you can find her sitting in an Adirondack chair with a book. She also loves to travel, swim, sail, and paddle a canoe around a quiet lake.

We would love to be a part of your Star System!

Get a daily dose of fun or inspiration on our Facebook page at
https://www.facebook.com/InspiredTogetherTeachers

Join other teachers for conversations on our private Teacher
Warriors Facebook Group at
https://www.facebook.com/groups/teacherwarriors

We are on Twitter as Inspired Together Teachers @TYTtribe

Love Instagram? Find us at Inspired Together Teachers.

Get free resources and support for your teaching journey on our blog
at   https://thrivingyoungteachers.com

Learn more about discounted bulk book purchases for your district
or PLC, speaking engagements, or our mentoring curriculum at
https/www.inspiredtogetherlearning.com

**"There are no educators that have greater knowledge and
experience in the field of education than Paula and Michele.
Not only are they knowledgeable and competent, but perhaps
more importantly, they both have a personal commitment to
excellence in education.
Simply stated, their hearts are in it."**

**Kirk Nigro, Educational Consultant, former Principal and
Superintendent, Ishpeming, Michigan**

Made in the USA
Middletown, DE
12 May 2021